The Celtic My
Collection

Other Books by Irish Imbas Books

The Celtic Mythology Collections

The Celtic Mythology Collection 2016
The Celtic Mythology Collection 2017

The Beara Trilogy:

Beara: Dark Legends

The Fionn mac Cumhaill Series:

Defence of Ráth Bládhma
Traitor of Dún Baoiscne
The Adversary

The Liath Luachra Series:

Liath Luachra: The Grey One
Liath Luachra: The Swallowed

Short Story Collections

The Irish Muse and Other Stories

The Celtic Mythology Collection 2018

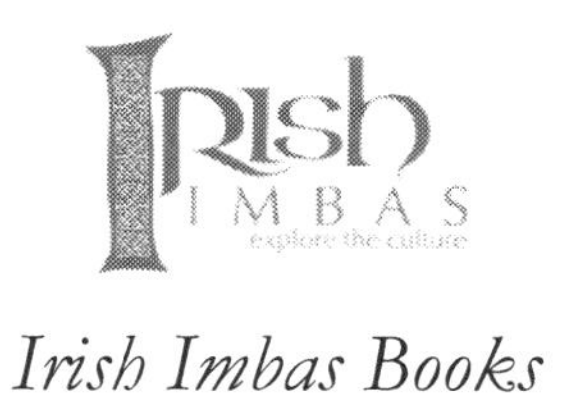

Irish Imbas Books

This is a work of fiction. Names, characters and incidents are products of the author's imagination or are used fictitiously and are not to be construed as real. Any resemblance to actual events, organizations or persons, living of dead, is entirely coincidental.

ISBN: 978-0-9951079-4-6

If you'd like to receive **Vóg, our monthly newsletter,** with articles on future books and projects we're working on, aspects of the creative process, bits and bobs on Irish mythology and more, please feel free to sign up at the Irish Imbas Books website: **irishimbasbooks.com**.

ACKNOWLEDGEMENTS

Special thanks to Marie Elder.

Cover design (Labhraidh Loingseach) by Brian Mahy.

Table of Contents

Irish Mythology Versus Celtic Fantasy:

One night at a party years ago I was introduced to a woman who proudly informed me she'd named her baby daughter 'Banshee' in celebration of her Irish heritage. Even at the time I was pretty stunned by this revelation. For an Irish person (and I would have thought most people would have known this), this was the equivalent of naming your daughter 'Death'.

About two weeks later, at another party (I had a social life back then!), I was cornered by a different woman asking for a translation to the chorus from Clannad's haunting *Theme Song from Harry's Game.* The Irish lyrics for the chorus had been written on her CD sleeve as 'Fol dol de doh fol-de de day' which she was convinced had a profound mystic and mythological meaning. Needless to say, she wasn't too impressed when I translated it as 'La, la la la, la la lah'.

These are just two examples of the cultural disconnect between Irish people and non-Irish people who dabble in Irish mythology. They are however only two of the hundreds I've experienced over the last twenty years or so and I know many other people who've had similar experiences. In some respects, it's been a source of continual bemusement to see how bizarrely and inaccurately our culture's been represented over that time.

To be honest, Clannad probably bear some responsibility for the situation given that their moody *Robin of Sherwood* and other songs (aided in equal amounts by 'Celtic' films such as *Excalibur* and others) helped to create this situation. During the 1970s and 1980s, with the explosion of fantasy entertainment through books, comics and movies, stories based on Celtic mythology suddenly became extremely hip. Atmospheric visuals and music from musicians such as Clannad, Enya and others were used to help fan the flames to the point where entertainment based on 'Celtic Mythology Fantasy' (what some call 'Celtic Fantasy') is now a major industry.

Celtic Mythology = ?

Unfortunately, the term 'Celtic Mythology' is a bit of a misnomer. The main problem is that the terms 'Celtic' or 'Celt' don't actually mean anything, and therefore can mean whatever you want them to mean. Certainly, back in early Europe there were populations with similar cultural characteristics that the Romans generically referred to as 'Celts' but even amongst those peoples there were substantial cultural differences. In a sense, using the word 'Celt' is a bit like using the word 'European'. Modern-day Europe covers a defined geographical area with populations that have many similar characteristics but, again, the truth is that it's the differences that define them. A German, for example, wouldn't primarily identify himself/herself as a European. Neither would a French person. Or a Welsh person. Or an Irish person.

Another problem with 'Celts' is that the ancient cultures referred to as 'Celtic' (always by people who didn't form part of those cultural group) are pretty much gone, eradicated by the Romans or subsequently colonized out of existence. Because records of the Celts are extremely sparse, many people steer towards the closest thing (Gaelic records or Welsh records) instead. Unfortunately, because of their age, the cultural context in these records is very broadly interpreted and their modern-day expression tends to reflect the particular bias of the people interpreting them.

The Salmon of Ignorance

Several years ago, my family attended a friend's 'Celtic' wedding which turned out to be some strange mix of Revisionist Celt, New Age, Wicca and other influences. It was a great celebration and we were having a lot of fun until the marriage ceremony proper began and the celebrants started praying to the Salmon of Knowledge. At that point, my kids started cracking up and I was struggling to keep a straight face myself.

It was immediately obvious what had happened. In their attempts to 'Celticise' the ritual, the celebrants had clearly gone through various 'Celtic' books (Gaelic books, in this case) and selectively pulled out elements that they could incorporate. Unfortunately, because they were oblivious to the cultural context, what they eventually ended up with made absolutely no sense and the poor old salmon was elevated to some kind of symbolic messenger of the Gods. Recently, my daughter told me that, for her, it was like going to a church as a kid and discovering that everyone was praying to Kermit the Frog.

This is the common pattern you'll find in any modern "Celtic Fantasy" that incorporates Irish mythology. A non-Irish author/film-maker or other creative type will browse through some 'Celtic' source material, pluck out a few cultural elements and then rearrange them with other non-related elements to create a commercial narrative.

Appropriation and Exploitation: Wading in the cultural shallows

The problem, however, is that mythology is CULTURALLY based. Because it's culturally based, many of the mythological elements and associated context have been passed down through generations and incorporated into national identity and belief systems. Today of course, the use of Irish mythology has been superseded by scientific rationale, but its core narratives remain intrinsically linked to Ireland's self-identity and cultural values.

From an Irish perspective therefore, when you see your native cultural icons plucked from their normal environment, repackaged in some pseudo-Celtic nonsense and reproduced out of context in a fantasy product, you can start to appreciate the complaints from other native groups about the commercial exploitation of their cultures. For Irish people in particular, it feels as though we've been bombarded by mawkish, overly romanticised and culturally inaccurate interpretations of our own mythology for decades.

Even today, if you really want to bug an Irish friend, try showing him or her a copy of *Darby O' Gill and The Little People* (starring that famed 'Irish' actor … Sean Connery) or perhaps a section from the execrable *Mystic Knights of Tir Na nÓg* (a kind of 'Oirish Transformers' television series). Alternatively, you could share the 'Disneyfied' commercial version of Fionn mac Cumhaill created by the British National Trust Board at the Giants Causeway or read them any number of twee 'Oirish Fairytales'. The choices are truly endless but some of these commercial products are so culturally offensive they should have been put down at birth.

Kickback

Over the last few decades, within all genres, we've seen increasing numbers of English-speaking creatives explore other 'exotic' cultures as a source of creative inspiration. More recently, however, we've also seen increasing kickback from ethnic minorities (and majorities) at the continued misrepresentation of their cultures. This situation, I think, reflects a shift in that consumers are cottoning onto the fact that many of the 'cultural' stories they're being presented with aren't entirely genuine. It also reflects increased scrutiny and accountability from people whose cultural mythology/belief systems are being misrepresented. In the fantasy genre, you may recall the recent furore associated with J. K. Rowling's portrayal of Navajo belief systems in *History of Magic in North America*. Keep an eye out because you'll probably be seeing an increasing number of similar response over the years to come.

I don't really believe it's any creator's intention to be offensive when they use mythologies not associated with their own cultures. In fact, I'd suspect the majority of them would be dismayed if they knew their work was somehow considered offensive. Unfortunately, people tend to tell stories based on their own experiences or what they've managed to learn and, frankly, sometimes you just don't know what you don't know. Different cultures aren't easily transferable (although if you spend enough time living in them or studying them, it certainly helps) and this makes wading in the mythological shallows that much more dangerous. This is particularly the case with Irish mythology as there's already so much misinformation out there (many people, for example, through no fault of their own, still believe W. B. Yeats is a credible authority on Irish mythology).

Neither do I believe that Irish people have a particular aversion to non-Irish authors fantasy creators developing products based on Irish mythology. That said, it would probably help if they acknowledged the source material and tried to get even the most basic cultural context correct. Unfortunately, many 'Celtic Fantasy' authors and film-makers don't, and in some cases their idea of cultural authenticity is to chuck in some Irish names and a smattering of Gaelic – a language they neither speak nor understand, and care even less about getting grammatically correct. Given all of this, it's no surprise that Celtic Fantasy has such a bad name among Irish consumers.

And this is probably one of the saddest ironies about this situation. If you look up any 'Irish mythology' or 'Celtic fantasy' book list, you'll struggle to find a single Irish author (although you'll find plenty of Paddywhackery). This is because most of those authors are non-Irish authors writing a commercial kind of 'Oirish' mythology fiction for American/Canadian/Australian etc. markets. They are not writing for an Irish audience. As a result, you now have a bizarre situation where Irish/Gaelic culture is used as a commercial commodity for a non-Irish/non-Gaelic consumer base.

Go figure!

A Tough Call

Watching the recent upsurge in protests against publishers, film producers and popstars, it's no real surprise to see parallel occurrences with Irish people increasingly pouring online scorn on fantasy creatives who couldn't be bothered to get the basics right or who try to portray themselves as authorities on something they clearly don't understand. With Irish (and Sottish and Welsh etc.) creators now finally starting to reassume control of their own mythology/cultural heritage, it's more than likely that clashes between 'authentic Irish' and 'commercial Oirish' are only going to increase from here on in. This is a shame because, at heart, the issue's really about how much leeway the argument of 'creative licence' allows you to go in terms of misrepresenting someone else's culture for your own gain. That's a tough call, as it comes down to an individual's personal values, experience and judgement. People will always be inspired by aspects of different cultures, and there's no harm in using those – provided it's done honestly. Sadly, given that there's no real consensus on this at present, for the next few years you can probably expect to keep encountering young girls called 'Death' obliviously wreaking cultural havoc.

Brian O'Sullivan (Wellington, 2018)

Moireach

Donna Rutherford

The first time I saw my father shed his skin I was barely eight.

On the shore of Camas Uig, under the white light of a midsummer moon his sealskin slid to the sand, leaving him naked and pale.

Can you imagine the shock of it? I was practically a bairn. It's a good thing I was born with special powers myself. Here on the Isle of Lewis I think it's safe to say that I, Moireach Rutherford, am well informed in the ways of the magic folk.

***

'Come in there, our Moireach.' Father Quinlan's eyebrows exit the confessional before the rest of his face.

'Good morning, Father, and thank you.'

'Sit down, child.' A chair creaks on the other side of the partition as Father Quinlan settles. In the dim light, his bald pate gleams through the iron grill.

'Bless me, Father for I have sinned.' I might be the only Catholic changeling in Scotland. I hear a slow sigh; Father must have had his quota of sinners this afternoon.

'Go ahead, Moireach, what's it to be today?'

What's it to be today? Where's the usual *confess my child?* This is like ordering a fish supper. 'Father,' I clear my throat. 'Father, I…' I smell onions from his lunchtime sandwich.

'Go on, dear.'

His voice is terribly kind, and I remember why I like coming to confession. Aside from Daddy, Father Quinlan is the only person on Lewis whose eyes say the same as his mouth.

'Well, as you know, Father, my Daddy is a Selkie.'

Another slow exhale, poor Father is exhausted.

'I'm going to tell him I know. You see, if he knows that I know his secret, then he might take me with him to meet my mother.'

I see Father's hand come to rest on his shiny head. Like he's holding onto the top should it fall off, full up with people's sins like it must be.

'Moireach, did you want to confess today?'

'Oh no. Not really, Father, it's more a chat I was after. Although to be honest, I did have mean thoughts earlier.'

'Mean thoughts is it?' He sounds relieved.

'Well, just a few. About Innis, the boy that works at the Co.' I try not to get cross with people. Heaven knows what my powers could do if unleashed.

'Go on, Moireach.'

The confessional groans as father shifts in his chair. Does his poor back ache? They really should upgrade him to a lazy boy. A red one. 'Oh, it's nothing really, Father. It's just, I went in today for a packet of Hula Hoops, and a Cola. He was doing that thing.'

'What thing is that, Moireach?'

'He holds my purchases at arm's length like they might give him some deadly disease. He says, *There's your change Mad Mo. Away and put it in your cauldron.*'

'Sticks and stones…'

'Will break my bones, I know. It's okay, Father. I hexed him on my way out. Tomorrow he'll sport a fine pimple on the end of his nose.'

Father makes a sound like he's choking.

'Shall I do a few Hail Mary's? Anyway, I know you've had a long day, but can we talk about my Daddy?' I sense resistance.

'I'm fairly sure, Mo, that Davie isn't a Selkie.'

'Ah, you say that now, Father, but all the signs are there. I've seen it with my own eyes.'

'Didn't you tell me you'd dreamed it, Mo. We get in difficulties when we confuse our dreams with the real world.'

What do they teach these men at priest school? Doesn't he know dreams are echoes. 'The issue here is, should I tell Daddy I know? And if so, how?' My skin prickles at the idea of swimming with him. That finally it'll all be out in the open and we might swim off and visit her. 'Father, I'm sure by now he knows I'm a changeling.' The silence is loud and a little worrying. 'Has he spoken to you of it?' I lower my voice so as to demonstrate my discretion. 'Has he mentioned my special powers?'

There's a scrape preceded by a shuffle as Father – quite against protocol – stands and moves the grate aside. As I look up from my prostrate position it strikes me, he should trim his nose hair.

'Mo, can I come around?'

'Of course, Father.' He does, and I sit on the stool to face him.

'Davie,' he clears his throat, examining the fingers of his left hand. Does he wish there were a ring there? 'Davie, is a simple man. He doesn't pay mind to stories and imaginings.'

'But...'

'Mo, the only things Davie talks to me about are the football scores, and the fishing. He certainly thinks you're special, but as for powers, I'd say not. Take my advice, Mo.' He pats my arm like I might be a wee dog. 'Keep these stories to yourself, don't worry Davie.'

I tell Father I've no intentions of worrying Daddy. In fact, my intentions are quite the opposite. I plan to make life easier for everyone.

***

The walk home seems to take an awful long time. I'd change into a hawk if I'd the energy, but hexing Innis has me wiped out. I choose the longer route, away from the village and along the beach.

I'm barefoot because it's Tuesday. The sky is a soupy grey and briny air stings my eyes and nose. A jaggy shell digs into the soft space between my toes and I stop, sitting on the shingle to remove it. A sticky trickle of blood colours the sand stuck to my white feet.

I've no memory of walking. I don't like to touch the water, it makes me reckless. But my toes are submerged, and icy flow runs up and around my sore foot. Trails of maidenhair seaweed stroke and weave in figures of eight around my ankles. I raise my eyes to the horizon, filled with something that might be happiness. And there, at the point my eyes fix, bobbing on the rolling grey waves is a single sleek head. A seal with the darkest eyes, ebony pools of words I can almost hear. I'm shaking like Lachie Munroe's hands after a night on the whisky, and the water's lapping around my knees. I hear my name and know she's calling to me: *Moireach, my Moireach, come Moireach.*

'Jesus, Mo, what are you doing?'

Daddy's here. Where did he spring from? He's grabbing my shoulders, his fingers digging into the tender flesh where my wings sprout. 'Are you mad, lass?' His arms are round me, pulling me back till we're on the sand and shingle facing the sea.

'I saw her out there.'

The arms around my waist drop and he turns away.

'Daddy, I did. Right there.' I point, but of course she's gone.

'Come on, Mo, let's go home.' He's walking, head down, hands rooted deep in his pockets. 'The rain's not far away.'

I hurry to catch him, my foot stinging and stripey leggings wet. 'Daddy, will you not just look.' His head hangs like a sad dog. 'You never look anymore.'

***

Our house is small, some might say cramped. I like to keep things and Daddy doesn't complain. Shelves, window sills, mantlepiece and cupboards hold thirteen years' worth of shells, dried seaware, broken china and other treasures. The beach is a veritable feast for a collector such as myself. The seaware smells like bad fish for a few days as it dries, but you get used to it.

Daddy lights the fire, and turns, I watch the flame dance on his face. His lips part just so, as if a word wants set free. His eyes flicker in the glow and he runs a hand over his face, like he's wiping away a memory. That word on his lips gets trapped inside, like all his other words.

'Get changed, Mo, I'll fix supper.'

Sometimes, my heart hurts looking at him. His mantle of sadness is heavy. It's a mystery to me, all the sadness, because surely when he dons his sealskin he finds her again.

***

It's TV dinner again. We eat cod and potatoes from plates on our laps, watching the news. He doesn't want to talk to me. It wasn't always this way. I must go swimming with him soon, because it's getting where I can't hardly remember how it was - before.

I was eight when she found her sealskin.

I'm tired of the news and sick of the fish. 'May I leave the…couch? I'm full up.'

His dark brows draw together in a frown, 'You've hardly eaten a thing.'

'I've homework to do.' This line always works. They told him I need extra support at school, that I've got an aspergerism. I'm a changeling for heaven's sake, 'isms' are the least of my concerns.

***

My bed is covered with a patchwork quilt. It's old and very soft, worn in places and a little faded. I curl in a wee ball and bury my face into the warm folds. I forget about Innis at the Co, Father Quinlan's oniony breath, and the throb between my toes from the jaggy shell. I remember the silky head in the dancing waves.

The sky is an inky weave of black and blue, and I'm padding down to the shoreline. Four feet and a coat of warm fur. What am I? Socks of white on russet red, and the brush of a tail in the chill air. No moon, no chance of a reflection on water. But my eyes are sharp in the dark and there are new smells with each frosty breath.

I hear voices by the water. Still as the night, I watch and wait. There, by the tide line, a row of people look out. Waist deep is a man like Father Quinlan, he holds a cup high above his head. A blanket of quiet settles over the island. Even the waves are still.

'Seonaidh, I give thee this cup of ale, hoping that thou will be so good as to send us plenty of seaware for enriching our ground in the coming year.'

His voice is deep and sure. He tips the cup into the water, the silence lifts and the congregation form a procession back to the village, candles in hands, faces alight with quiet joy. I wait in the shadows, wondering if Seonaidh the water spirit might make an appearance. He doesn't. My Daddy does.

By the edge of the shore he walks slowly, as though he carries a terrible weight. I'm about to run to him, to tell him it's me: Moireach. But my voice is a whimpering bark, and he walks on. From the far edge of the water trots a horse. I've never seen one like it, certainly not on Lewis. Its snowy coat glows in the moonlight, on its back is a leather saddle, and a bridle of silver, glinting as it trots soundlessly over pebbles and seashells. Daddy lifts his heavy head and smiles, as if the bonny horse has been sent to save him.

Dear God, it's then that I know. I run toward them, but I've had no time to get used to my fox legs. I try to cry out, but he pays no mind. Holding the silver bridle, he lifts himself on to the horse. Too late, oh too late, for that's no horse. Oh Daddy, you should have known.

The Kelpie shudders, its mane rippling, and settling. It turns to the water and gallops, hooves cutting the tide line and into the depths in four wild strides. Daddy doesn't look back, doesn't move, stuck by magic to the Kelpie, who won't stop till he reaches the bottom of the ocean floor. There, he'll devour poor Daddy, leaving his liver to float to the surface as a warning.

I run back and forth, back and forth along the water's edge, pleading for Seonaidh to help me, for the Faeries, Selkies, and Wulvers to intervene. But the fox has no words. Fireflies dance above the waves, golden dots of sparkling light, flickering and weaving. A Will o' the Wisp. Death approaches.

In human form, my voice returns with wonderful force. 'Daddy! Daddy. Come back, Daddy!'

He's there by my bed, hands on my shoulders, shaking me awake.

'Moireach, you're alright lass. It's a dream, just a dream.'

I throw my arms around him and he pulls me into his lap like he did before. I curl there and let my eyes flow like the sea, remembering a thousand nights when I slept this way. Nights after the sea took her.

***

It's a terrible long wait till Sunday. It needs to be Sunday because it's the seventh day of the week. Ideally, I should wait till the seventh month for maximum good fortune, but Daddy is acting strangely. I must take his wellbeing into my own hands.

I study the colour photograph in my library book carefully, then read the notes for the seventy-seventh time. It's a Scottish wildlife encyclopaedia from the *not to be issued* section. I used a little magic on Mrs Nesbitt the librarian – she's a special friend of Father Quinlan's. She asked if I wouldn't rather take home a nice piece of fiction: *perhaps Judy Bloom, Moireach*, she said. When I told her I was studying seals her eyes went watery. She patted my hand and slid the book across the counter. Sometimes my magic is stronger than I realise.

My fingers are long, with no sign of webbing. The same goes for my feet. If I concentrate enough and try to think like a seal – when my toes touch the water next - I might shapeshift into one. It has to work. It's the lynch pin in my plan.

***

At 11pm, I hear the soft pad of Daddy's feet move across the wood floor. He thinks I don't hear, thinks I don't know he slips out barefoot each night and goes to the water. I count seven seconds and sneak from my room, past the fire and its dying embers, out the door, and down the steps without a single sound.

He's moving quickly, already out the garden and on the dirt path that leads to the beach. I keep him in sight, creeping like a shadow. My nerves zing like the magic coursing in my veins.

Where the path opens out to the sand I crouch behind a bush and wait. I'll run to him at the perfect moment – just as he climbs into his seal suit. I'll tell him it's okay. I'll step into the water and trust my magic will transform me. All the sadness will float away with the tide and we'll swim to her.

Head down and hands deep in his pockets, he walks to the water's edge. He stops and raises his face to the moon. No sign of his seal suit, not yet. He checks his watch and looks to his right. Oh my, this is a development I hadn't dared dream of. Is he going to summon her? His eyes are on the ocean. Why didn't I think of it? Seven tears of a loved one to summon the Selkie.

I'm shaking like Lachie Munroe again, shivering although the night is mild. I keep my eyes on Daddy and the ocean and hug myself, praying to Seonaidh to let her come. Let her come.

Just like that he turns, away from the water, away from the place where she'll appear. He walks along the tideline, stride sure, head up, hands no longer in his pockets.

A voice calls out: a woman, further down the beach. She's hurrying toward him. She has not come from the ocean. She has no sealskin to shed.

There's a terrible weight in my belly, like I've swallowed a rock. It tears from the inside. He holds out his arms and she runs to him. A kiss. I'm on my knees on the shingles. I should look away but my eyes won't let me. It's only silhouettes, shadows in the moonlight, but he strokes her hair tenderly and kisses her again.

It is not the right picture. I'm dreaming, like before. Daddy and Irene Rowan from the primary school.

The light has changed. I'm curled in a ball, under the stunted branches of the bush. It is the darkest part of the night, before the dawn. On the beach, there is no Daddy, no Will o' the Wisp or Wulver, no Kelpie, or Selkie. There is no-one.

By the water's edge I watch. Gentle waves, calm and dark. The sea glints and ripples as a finger of moonlight pierces the surface, lighting the messy undertow. The water winks; things are not as they seem. I am not as I was.

I stare at that place where light meets dark, till the ocean in my eyes is all dried out. Kneeling where the sea kisses the sand, I trail a finger through the cool tide. It draws back in a breath, and I think it might be waiting. I nod at the black line that ties ocean to sky. 'That's me away then.'

***

All the way home I don't turn around, not once. Over the fence and through the dewy grass I walk in a fine rhythm, eight steps at a time. A nicer number, well-rounded and symmetrical. At the back door, I pause for eight seconds then turn the handle.

Daddy stands, tired-eyed by the stove, lighting the flame below the kettle. When I cough he starts, dropping the lit match, lifting his finger to his mouth where the flame burned. 'Mo.' He runs the heel of his hand up and over his brow.

'Good morning, Daddy.'

His eyes flick to the closed door of my room, and his forehead lines in a frown. 'I thought you were sleeping.'

'I was.' I rub the salt from my cheeks. 'Then, I went walking.'

Nodding slowly, he relights the match. The flame greets the gas with a burst of blue and gold, licking up over the edges of the kettle, spreading its glow. And I feel it, inside. Like that very match is spreading its warmth through my belly, working its flickery, bright glow up past my heart. And, then I'm smiling. A real smile that wants to tell him with all the words I don't have, that it's okay.

I watch as my smile passes as if by magic, from me to him. Then I'm in his arms, burrowing my face into the smell of his old shirt. He strokes my hair with a rough hand, and the kettle begins to whistle spirals of hot steam in the briny air.

Mythological Context: The Selkie

Due to the close association between water and the spiritual world in ancient times, the Otherworld was often considered to be located underwater (usually in the sea but also accessible through lakes and rivers) and there are numerous old stories and folklore associated with this belief. It's no surprise therefore, that a number of narratives subsequently came into being involving creatures who lived underwater. These were predominantly known as the *maighdean marra* [mermaid] and *fear mara* [merman] but they behaved and operated within the established constraints associated with '*Na Sidhe*', that is, linked to the dead and potentially dangerous to humans.

These underwater creatures were very different to the more contemporary interpretation of what's commonly known as the mermaid: a creature with a human torso and a fish-like tail. The latter are based on elements from Assyrian tales, the Greek sirens and other, later, influential narratives such as Hans Christian Andersen's 'The Little Mermaid'. Elements of these overseas stories did enter Ireland, Scotland and Wales from medieval times and are thought to have had some influence on the portrayal of the original Celtic mythological creatures.

One of the most common stories involving the *maighdean mara* tells of a young man who spots a beautiful woman on the sea shore. When the woman puts her magic cloak aside, the man seizes it, thus taking her under his power. Accompanying him home, the *maighdean mara* becomes his wife and they have a number of children. One day, one of those children discovers the magic cloak, which had been hidden by the young man, and returns it to his mother. Taking the cloak, she flees back to the sea and enters it, never to be seen again. Variations of this legend are believed to have spread to Scotland and Iceland in the late Middle Ages.

Up in the Orkney Islands and the Western Isles of Scotland, these stories appear to have developed into a more specialised lore around a seal people called Selkie (the word 'selkie' is thought to be an old Orcadian dialect for "grey seal") although those tales are also found in other parts of Scotland and Ireland. Much of the more common lore with respect to selkie seems to have been sourced specifically from the works of a nineteenth century Orkney writer, Walter Traill Dennison, who wrote a number of tales based on beliefs and traditions from that area, many of them overly romanticised and probably differing from the original lore as a result of the transfer to prose. The most prominent theme to this selkie folklore relates to their shapeshifting ability: they are seals who can take on human form by removing their skin or pelt. If that skin is lost or taken, the selkie is restricted to human form until it is recovered.

After publishing two collections that included a selkie story, we were reluctant to add yet another selkie this time around. Unfortunately, Donna Rutherford's cheerfully hilarious *Moireach* was simply too good to ignore.

Brian O'Sullivan

Homecoming

Damien J Howard

It was still early in the morning when she saw it glinting in the sunlight and dancing above the grass in the field. It was like a tiny little sun, a small ball of perfect light blazing in the morning air. It was a glorious clear autumn day, the leaves in the trees were starting their turn and Doireann had already completed the early morning chores for the day. The rest of it was hers, and hers alone.

She ran out into the fields leaving her parent's farmhouse behind her; leapt over the old and collapsing rock wall, then into the rolling fields where her father kept the sheep and cattle. Here she would invent entire worlds of secret princesses, of which she was one, and dashing princes that would come to rescue her from unseen evil.

When she saw it first it stopped her dead in her tracks. Her imagined quest to escape the evil dungeon sank away and was replaced by the insatiable curiosity of this tiny dancing ball of light. Doireann moved closer. She had worked with animals all her short life and knew not to startle it with any with sudden movements. She approached carefully, her hands and fingers rolled out as wide as possible. She tiptoed like a girl on a tightrope until she was close enough to see it better.

Then the ball moved away, bouncing on the wind, no, *against* the wind, moving away from her. She followed; she had to know what this magnificent ball of light was. It kept its pace ahead of her, moving fast and she had to break into a run to keep it in sight. It moved over and across the rolling hills until it swung over the next rock wall and into Old Field. Doireann skidded to a halt at the edge of the wall and peered in.

Old Field was a place her father had told her many stories of by dim light before bedtime. The field had never been tilled, never been grazed by any beast ever in her family's history, but the field was theirs. The grass grew long and large sharp stones protruded from the earth to try and touch the sky. The place had taken on a different meaning to little Doireann, a fabled place where the wild imaginings of a child met the superstitions of adults in a way that she didn't really understand.

There she saw the little ball of light dancing among the tall grass and moving around the boulders and rocks, beckoning her to join. And so she did. She climbed up onto the rock wall and jumped down into the tall grass.

As she did the ball of light moved deeper into Old Field and Doireann followed. In the grass she could see the markings of many fairy rings dotted around, no stone seemed to break them in their near perfect symmetry. Doireann knew it very bad fortune to disturb a fairy fort, even the gods of nature knew that.

The ball moved around them, in and out, circling them with little regard, pulling Doireann deeper and deeper into Old Field. Then she saw it, where she was being led. In the centre of a crop of stones, overgrown by grass and moss, was a large Cairn made of tall flat stones angled together with a larger one balanced over the top. This ancient monument stood against the untamed wilderness around it and survived. The builders long lost to time.

In the centre of this Cairn, where the rocks met, a small passage led into darkness and that is where the little ball of light hovered, waiting.

Doireann approached and as she did the ball vanished inside the Cairn. She pressed her hands up against the cold stone and felt a draft of air coming from the tiny space between the rocks. There was nothing but darkness there now, and no sign of the light. Then she heard a whisper on the wind calling her name. 'Doireann ...' it hissed.

She moved in closer to try and see the little ball of light that called to her. She pressed herself against the rock, squeezing her shoulder to it, peering deep into the darkness ahead. She found now that the rock seemed less rigid, its once rough surface feeling more elastic so that she was able to push her tiny self further and further inside, the rock moving and contorting around her.

Still she heard her name on the wind. She felt a sudden claustrophobia and a fear rose in her gut as the darkness inside the Cairn enveloped her. She advanced nevertheless, determined to discover the mystery of the light. She pushed through her fear and let the yearning for discovery take over.

In a flash of brilliant light, she found the rock open up again and she fell out on the other side of the Cairn. It took her eyes a moment to adjust to these new surroundings. The grass beneath her feet and hands was white, a pure white like snow. The trees in the distance were made of grey trunks and branches and magnificent white leaves.

She looked up at the sky and lost her breath at its beauty. The stars were so vivid in a sky cast in deep purple and dark blue. A falling star streaked across the heavens leaving a trail of golden dust to seemingly fall through the cosmos.

Even though it appeared like night, it was warm in this strange land that looked like nothing she'd ever seen before. She wanted to capture it all in her mind, so beyond her own imagination it was.

'Doireann.' The voice said again, clearer now. It was a soft feminine voice. She looked behind her and saw the woman sitting on a perfectly round grey rock in the field beside the Cairn which now looked new, all the surfaces of it carved with intricate infinity spirals. The woman was tall and thin with milky white skin. Her long hair was silver and it sparkled in the light, her eyes a piercing baby blue. She wore a light blue flowing dress embroidered with the same infinity symbols in white pearls. She smiled at the little girl and rose gracefully from her perch. 'Welcome home sweet child. I am Clíodhna. I'm very happy you followed me home.'

Doireann picked herself up and stood looking at the woman called Clíodhna who also rose from her perch on the stone. She moved with a graceful ease as though she was floating, not stomping around like Doireann who heard the white grass crack beneath her.

'Where am I?' the little girl asked.

'You are home. Do you not remember this place?'

Doireann shook her head. She knew she'd remember if she'd ever seen something like this before.

'Maybe the memories will return. This is your home.' Clíodhna reached over and rested her perfect hand on the girl's shoulder. 'You are so much bigger now than when you left.'

'Are you a fairy?' Doireann asked, trying to make sense of what she was seeing. The woman had no wings but she had a sense about her, something not from the world that Doireann knew.

'We have many names. We serve Danann, we are many and we are hidden.' She spoke softly, 'And you are one of us.'

Again, Doireann shook her head, 'No, I'm just a girl.' She insisted.

Clíodhna moved around her, her long dress flowing over the white grass. 'No child, you are so much more. Let me tell you a story,' she said softly. 'There was once a girl called Doireann, but that was not you. You are a child of this place.' She held out her hands to encompass the world around her, the fields and the white forest beyond. 'But children of this place still need the milk of human mothers, and so you were taken to their world, made shape like a human child and swapped for the babe at the woman's breast.'

'That's not true!' Doireann insisted, stomping her feet into the crackling white grass.

Clíodhna loomed large before the girl, casting her shadow wide. 'You wouldn't have been able to cross into this world if it were not true. You are a changeling, but soon you will return to us in your true form.'

She had heard the stories, her mother had told her of babies taken in the night and replaced by a fairy changeling. But she had been baptised, only unholy children could be taken. But what if it happened before that? What if she was taken before her baptism? Not her, the real Doireann. Could it be true?

'No! I'm me! I know I'm me!' Doireann insisted. She wanted to run, but to where? 'Take me home!'

'You have no home there anymore.' Clíodhna said as she moved around Doireann to block her path to the Cairn. 'You will join us here, become one of us, grow and thrive to serve Danann as we do. And you will forget that world and the people there. They are nothing to you. Not anymore. You are so much more than them now.' Her smile hid a tone of authority that unnerved Doireann, she had heard it before in certain adults of the cloth who told stories of kind things to hide a bleak truth.

She was a fairy, a creature of great power, if only a child one for now. It was like the dreams she would have of discovering her great hidden power, but now that it was before her, she didn't want it. She wanted her life back, the simple one on the farm with her mother and her father and all the animals.

'No!' Doireann proclaimed and started to run. She ran away from the Cairn and the woman, Clíodhna. She didn't know where she was going or if she was being chased, but she ran for a treeline she could see not too far away.

She burst through the white foliage and fell down a steep dip in the earth. Here the contrast of the grey trees and white leaves was more stark against the colour of the earth beneath her, which looked more like perfect yellow sand. Through the white canopy she could still see snatches of the purple and blue sky and the tapestry of stars.

Doireann picked herself up again and dusted herself down. The particles didn't simply fall off her but moved off like a cloud dancing in the air. Twirling around, she saw the dust move from her in intricate circular patterns.

The world started to spin in a haze of muted colours. When she stopped she saw a hound standing opposite her. It was magnificently black, its fur prickly like the back of a hedgehog and its eye like yellow crystals. She caught its eye and froze. She knew what to do if you saw a fox on the farm: if you were to startle it, it could lash out.

The hound didn't move, didn't make a sound, not even a snarl. It simply looked at her with its piercing eyes. Then it took a seat on the yellow sand and Doireann relaxed.

'He won't hurt you,' said a woman's voice from behind the dense trees. Doireann saw a shade of light pink moving through the forest.

When the woman appeared she looked similar to Clíodhna, but with golden hair and a pink dress. The hound sat proudly beside where the new woman came to rest. 'You look lost child. You look not of this world?'

'I chased a fairy into the rock and now I'm lost.' Doireann explained to the new stranger.

'A fairy…' The stranger smirked to herself. 'I was once like you. Tell me your name.'

'Doireann,' she said insistently, straightening her back.

'I'm Breena,' said the woman, 'Though that's not your real name.'

'It is!' Doireann insisted. She was fed up of people in this strange place telling her things. Seeing the girl's annoyance, Brenna took a step back. 'I don't want to be a fairy! I'm a person, I'm a girl, and I want to go home!'

Breena looked at Doireann from the corner of her eye. 'Who told you, you were one of our kin?' she enquired.

'The Fairy at the Cairn, she brought me here and now she won't let me go home! I want to go home!'

'Clíodhna,' the stranger whispered beneath her breath. The hound shrugged its nose, grunting at the mention of the name. 'She is a trickster. Don't listen to her.'

'I want to go home!' Doireann insisted. 'Can you bring me home?'

'Perhaps. But if Clíodhna brought you here, it was for a reason. She does not act without recourse. And she won't allow you to return easily.'

'I have to get home! My parents will be looking for me!' Doireann insisted, 'You have to help me. I'm not a changeling, I'm not a fairy, I'm just a girl and I want to go home!'

Breena moved fast, closing in towards Doireann. She grabbed the child by her chin, looking her face up and down. Doireann dug her feet deeper into the yellow sand. 'But what if she was telling the truth? What if you are one of us? If you stay in the world of men your powers will fade, you will never be able to come back here. Do you want to give all that up?'

Even though her head was held tightly by the stranger, Doireann managed to nod.

'And what of the real Doireann?' The stranger asked, much to the girl's confusion. The girl shook her head and Breena continued. 'I do not agree with the way they do things, but if you are what Clíodhna says then the real Doireann may be long gone, or she may already be returned.'

'I am the real Doireann!' The girl insisted, shaking free of Breena's grasp. 'I'm real, I'm real!' Her voice was raised to a shout and she saw the hound stand up on all fours to meet her tone. Doireann backed away from them both.

Breena paused and offered a smile. 'I can help you get back to the other world. If you follow me through the Cairn, we can distract Clíodhna. Do not listen to her, what she speaks are lies.'

'I want to go home now.'

'Then we go.' Breena gestured her to turn and move out of the forest. Doireann had to climb up the yellow embankment she had fallen down and drag herself back up to the verge with the white grass. She pulled herself beneath the white leaves until she was back into the field beneath the purple and blue stars dancing like a living beast above her. Across the field she could see the stone Cairn against it all, an entire universe up in the sky and, beneath it all, her only way home.

Doireann climbed to her feet as the hound and Breena appeared behind her. Breena knelt down and whispered into the hound's ear. It took off running across the long white grass towards the Cairn. Breena held out her hand for Doireann to take. 'Take my hand and follow me. Don't stop until you are back on the other side. Then run home and never try to return. Clíodhna has limited power in your world, so long as you never go near the Cairn again.'

The girl nodded and they started to walk across the field. Doireann couldn't see anything beyond the Cairn, as though it was standing at the edge of this strange and beautiful world and if you travelled too far beyond you'd simply fall off into the cosmos.

There, waiting on her stone as she was when Doireann first came through, was Clíodhna. The hound had run up to meet her and stood on guard close to her perch.

'What are you doing, Breena?' Clíodhna called out across the field.

'Stay with me,' Breena said to Doireann, ignoring the woman's call.

'This is dangerous,' Clíodhna continued. 'She belongs here with us, nothing good will come of her return! You'll only strand her there with nothing. It's already happened! It's been done!'

Doireann tried to ignore everything, she kept looking at the Cairn, at her way home from this place.

'Listen! Doireann!' Clíodhna changed her tactic to appeal to the girl instead. 'I know you're frightened, but I've been where you are now. I was once a changeling too. My own form was returned to their family. They'll have no place for you if you go! I know how it feels, but please believe me!'

'Don't listen to her,' Breena said. 'None of the children taken are ever returned. Until now. I will get you home before Clíodhna can replace you.'

They were getting closer now. Clíodhna tried to move towards them but the hound would snarl and growl at her, keeping her at bay.

'I'm not trying to hurt you!' Clíodhna pleaded to Doireann. 'She's tricking you. That's what she does!'

'It's you who are the trickster!' Breena spat at Clíodhna as they reached the Cairn. 'This has to stop, and I will stop you!' She swung around and bent down to Doireann. 'Go, go now, I'll hold open the way. And remember, never come back here.' She hugged Doireann and then rose.

The little girl turned and ran for the darkness between the rocks of the Cairn. The magnificent carved symbols on this side seemed to glow gold as she rested her hands on the surface. Just like before she started to push her way inside.

'What have you done?' The fading voice of Clíodhna, now a whisper on the wind, echoed to Doireann as she was taken into darkness once more.

A swift breeze hit her in the face, the chill that didn't exist in that other place suddenly impacting her as the light returned. She fell out of the impossibly small space between the Cairn and into the long grass of Old Field.

All around her she saw the fairy forts and rings and she jumped to her feet. She ran over towards the old stone wall, avoiding everything but the tall green grass until she was safety outside. Looking back over her shoulder she could see the old Cairn slumped in the centre of the field. She looked up at the sky as the last of the day's light began to fade and smiled at the clouds and the sun and the green trees and the brown earth.

She ran home, directed by the smoke rising from the chimney of her house. The day was gone and she'd be in trouble for missing her chores before dinner. They'd never believe her story, not in a million years, but she knew it was true. She was a fairy and if no one else would believe her that was fine, because she knew, and she was also just a girl, that she knew too, even if both were impossible.

Arriving at the house she turned the handle on the door, but it was locked. Inside she could hear the voices of her mother and father. She ran around to the back door, but something caught her eye in the window as she passed. She pressed her face to the glass and peered inside to her kitchen.

She wouldn't be in trouble for being late home. She was already there.

Doireann peered inside her own kitchen and saw herself sitting at the table. Her mother planted a kiss on her golden head as she picked up her spoon to eat. The other Doireann smiled back up at her and the family sat down to eat.

Outside, the little girl shrank from the window and backed away. She looked down at her hands and they were shaking. She felt thin, as though she was fading from the world. Looking over her shoulder, down the hill and towards the Old Field at the end of father's land, she felt a pang of sadness and of loss. Then confusion and anger began to boil inside her.

Who had just sat down to dinner, a changeling, or Doireann herself? And who was she? Her certainty only a few moments ago evaporated.

Over the grass field before her she caught a glimpse of a small ball of light, like a tiny star floating above the ground, beckoning her forward.

Mythological Context: Changelings

The belief in abduction of humans by Otherworld beings appears to have been quite prevalent in ancient Ireland with numerous references to young men and women being enticed away (sometime willingly, sometimes less so) in the remaining literature. For the former, such tales generally involved a situation where a human took an Otherworld lover (such as Niamh taking Oisín to Tír Na nÓg). For the latter, they usually entailed a hero warrior travelling to rescue a romantic love interest or some other dependent. Given the breadth and substance of these tales, it's also believed they were an extension of the beliefs prevalent throughout the society of the time, such 'departures' helping to make sense of unexplained deaths, disappearances and the unexpected deterioration of individuals that would have been so prevalent in those early communities.

With the coming of the written word (and Christianity) the Irish monks, when putting these Otherworld tales to paper (or vellum), initially treated them with respect for they formed fundamental elements of the belief system in the society where those authors were born and raised. As the Christian church grew in strength and influence however, the existence of two parallel belief systems became increasingly hard to maintain, particularly where they came into conflict. That situation was exacerbated by increasing pressure from the more established Church on the Continent. Far less accepting of native spiritual entities living alongside the officially sanctioned ones, the Continental section of the Christian Church would have been very keen to eradicate them.

The attitude to the Otherworld and its inhabitants underwent a lot of change over the following centuries, with increased condemnation and undermining of the native beliefs. One technique utilised by the Church in this regard was the use of biblical references to suggest that *Na Sidhe* (the Otherworld inhabitants) were actually fallen angels who'd been driven out of Heaven and were hence associated with the Devil. As a result, *Na Sidhe* were increasingly portrayed in a negative light, often depicted as malevolent and cruel or proactively seeking to injure human beings and replace them so that they could take their place in heaven. References in some 15th century manuscripts suggest that this attitude was firmly entrenched in Church teachings before the end of the Middle Ages.

Although the stories of abduction by *Na Sidhe* were already associated with unexplained deaths or disappearances, they became increasingly linked with the idea of 'replacement' and anyone who behaved unusually or outside the norms was often thought to have been replaced by a 'changeling' (a member of *Na Sidhe* in the individual's form). Although for the most part people balanced such beliefs with the reality of day-to-day existence, there were occasional cases that resulted in a grislier outcome. The most famous incident involving a belief in changelings was probably the infamous burning of Bridget Cleary by her husband in 1895. This incident received extensive coverage and had a huge influence in its day although more recent investigations suggest the burning was a murder associated with larger domestic conflict. To this day, individuals who display signs of erratic behaviour outside the norm are often described as being "away with the fairies".

Given the large child and infant mortality in agricultural communities, it was a logical consequence that changelings would also be associated with the abduction of children and there are many folktales and stories about the creatures replacing young infants and acting in a contrary manner (although some were the 'bogeyman-type' tales used to keep children in line). Boys, in particular, were believed to be subject to abduction by *Na Sidhe* not only because they were seen as a source of better labour for their Otherworld masters but also because of the age old, traditional idea that the male contributed more of his natural essence to the production of offspring, hence providing better 'replacement' value to Na Sidhe. In many 'Celtic' countries, this led to the practice of dressing infant boys in female clothing to confound the predatory changelings.

The theme of the 'replaced infant' is one found very often throughout medieval literature. Needless to say, the Church also encouraged the belief that those children who were baptised could not be taken by the Otherworld kidnappers.

Brian O'Sullivan

The Shadow of the Crow

Jerry Vandal

Kawmas was perched high in a tree, overlooking a mostly empty cemetery. He spent more time than he'd like to admit watching the living trying to reach out to the dead, but it was where he often found his mind would take him. Growing up, his dad had told stories he'd overheard the walkers tell about crows and death, and it fascinated Kawmas.

There was one walker sitting on the grass that caught his eye. He rarely interacted with walkers. He preferred to watch them although on occasion he'd venture from his perch, glide down to walkers and get close enough to hear them speak to slabs of granite. Typically, they would ignore him. *All those stories about death,* he would think. Today was different. As Kawmas watched his shadow grow long and touch him, the man spoke.

'This is my dad. He loved playing guitar,' the man said as he looked at Kawmas and introduced his father as if he were still alive and well. 'Watching him play and listening to him sing…' he stopped, looked down at the slab of granite and sighed. 'He seemed free.'

Kawmas approached the man slowly, not wanting to scare him. He too looked at the grave.

'Just to see this look in my dad's eyes,' the man continued as he thumbed a small piece of plastic. 'When he sat down and strummed his guitar and sung ... I don't know. He seemed at peace. Even if what he was singing sounded like he was hurting inside. I think it was one of the few ways he knew to let things out.' The man shifted his body and knelt in front of the flat rock. The bird skipped just beside him.

'I miss you dad. I miss you every day. Wish you were still here. I need you. For a lot of things.'

He took the flat piece of plastic and placed it in between the rock and the dirt and grass that surrounded it. 'I hope this finds you. I love you.'

Kawmas turned to watch the man stand up and look at him. 'I know you don't know me,' he said to Kawmas. 'But, if you can let my dad know I left him something, I'd appreciate it.' Sweeping at his pants, he caused the blades of grass that had stuck to him to fall back to the ground. Zipping up his jacket, he placed his hands in his pockets and left.

Kawmas gazed intensely at the item the man had left. It was a guitar pick the color of maple and the orange of a leaf in the fall, combined in a swirled pattern. He picked it up carefully in his mouth and tucked it under the feathers of his wing.

The crow flew back up to the tree he'd been perched on. Soon it would be the same colour as the pick. The man who'd set it down probably had many questions about the afterlife the crow could have answered. Crows couldn't talk to walkers about that other world but if he could, Kawmas would have said, *it's not paradise. It's not hell either. It just is, kind of like this place. The people, the passed, a lot are sad, some are angry, a few are happy. Mostly, they're still holding onto this world.*

As he sat in the tree, that was what he thought about: how there wasn't much difference between the people in the living world and the people in the dead world. The worlds were different, but the people were mostly the same. Kawmas decided he'd take the pick to the man's father. He hadn't travelled to the other world in almost a year and had done so then on a similar quest. That time, he'd been looking for a young woman whose father had left a small locket buried near her gravestone. Kawmas had dug it out and attempted to find the girl in the other world to give it her. It haunted Kawmas that he'd failed to do so.

'You know,' called another crow from a few branches higher. 'I get it,' he coughed. 'But I gave up.'

'Gave up?' Kawmas asked.

'Yeah. The whole delivering messages or that sentimental stuff to the afterlife deal,' the old crow said, staring off into the distance.

'Why's that? It's what we do,' Kawmas said, perplexed. He'd grown up knowing that it was the duty of the crow to travel between the worlds and let the dead know that they were remembered. Sometimes it was the only way they could let go and move on to find out what came after death. Long ago his ancestors had signaled the death of people in the living world. He wasn't sure what had changed, but now all crows were supposed to help the dead in the other world.

'No, it's what we try to do.'

'I don't follow,' Kawmas said.

'You're still young. I get it. And by no means do I want to discourage what you're trying to do. But when you get to my age you start to realize you can't fight what you are and what we are is screw ups.'

Kawmas thought about the previous year when he'd travelled to the other world. He'd truly wanted to find the young woman.

'That's a little pessimistic,' Kawmas said, fighting the urge to succumb to the futility that had prevented him from travelling to the other world for so long.

'That's reality. We've been that way. Always.'

'So, you're saying we shouldn't even try.' Kawmas looked down at the pick. A sprawl of nerves tightened in his wings and he sighed.

'I'm saying that it takes little to distract us from that. Honestly, I don't mean to convince you to stop trying. Just understand, it's our nature. And nature is hard to deter.' The old crow looked back at the sun, spread his wings and flew away.

Despite the old crow's words and his own fears, Kawmas decided he'd actually do this thing. He'd not just serve as the symbol of death crows had become known for.

The sun still had several more hours of duty however and he'd not be able to travel to the other world until it had set and the moon cast his shadow. The crow knew this just as he knew what he'd do, not so much to pass the time, but out of lonely habit: think.

And that's what Kawmas did.

At first, he tried to steer his thoughts: how nice a day it was, how it was to be enjoyed, especially with fall approaching. He enjoyed the fall more than summer. The sky would rarely wear the celestial blue it wore in the mid-year months, but he preferred the colder days of fall. He also liked to sit around and think and that somehow seemed far more acceptable during the fall than the summer.

After a while his mind whispered the thoughts he'd hoped to avoid, the thoughts he'd known would come knocking like an unwanted guest.

You're going to fail. Just as you've failed before. Just as crows always do.

Kawmas reflected on the previous year until the sun set. He took a moment to admire the red, orange, blue and whites as they came together to collectively say goodbye and goodnight and then he soared into the night. He was anxious to get to the other world. The sooner he got there, the sooner he'd find the man whose son had left him the pick. He soared briefly until he saw the moon and then angled himself so that his shadow touched the ground.

Kawmas pushed his wings together so that he resembled an arrow. The key to getting into the other world was to find its moon cast shadow, fly as hard and fast as he could and then as he neared the shadow, tuck his body so that he resembled a circle.

As Kawmas neared his shadow he closed his eyes and felt himself being sucked in, as though he were caught near a tornado. With only a few beats of his heart the crow was thrown into the world of the dead.

Shaking off the fall, he got to his feet and looked around. It was day in the other world. Nothing seemed to have changed. The dead, he realized, hated change. Even more so than those who walked freely and alive.

In the other world it was day, but it was still dark. There was no sun to light up that world. Each soul that walked around could only see what their soul would allow, which was at best determined by how much guilt a person carried inside of them. Less guilt seemed to mean they could see more, while those that felt its hold tended to fumble in the darkness. At least that's what Kawmas's father had told him when he sat him down and taught him about the worlds.

'Kawmas!' cawed another crow as Kawmas looked around the waiting land.

'Carwl,' Kawmas said with hesitation. He recognized his friend immediately and felt a hint of joy, but he also felt a sudden fear that his presence could deter him from getting the pick to the man in the life after. The last time he'd been with Carwl they'd got into a fight with a raven and Carwl had lost an eye.

'Good to see you crow, how you been?' Carwl asked.

'Been okay. You?'

'Ah, kind of tired of all this crap. Got a job delivering messages to the land of the waiting.'

Traveling to the other world was mostly an unwritten obligation among the crows. Due to a consistent lack of successful deliveries however, in recent years, a murder of crows had convened and created a system that guaranteed food for the crows to encourage more regular visits to the other world.

'So, you're working?'

'Actually, done for the day. Was planning to head over them hills there. There's a good-sized pond. I'll tell you, the water, nice kick to it if you know what I mean.'

'A kick to it?'

'Yesh, spiked with something. Hey, you have to join me,' Carwl said with an exaggerated tone on the 'have'.

'Sorry Carwl. I've something to take care of.'

'Come on, crow. How long has it been? Whatever it is, you can stop for a bit and have a drink. Frankly, just from looking at you, I think you could use one. Maybe six.'

'I really want to take care of this.'

'And you will.' Carwl dropped a wing over Kawmas. 'But first we drink. Then you can do whatever it is you came here to do. Besides, nobody here's going anywhere. Seriously, you look like you need someone to talk to. It's usually a little easier once you got something in you to help you focus. Come on.'

'Okay,' Kawmas said with regret.

'Ata boy.'

As the two birds took flight, Carwl guided Kawmas towards a forested hill. There they soon came to a pond just before a cluster of trees. 'I found this little spot a few months ago. Nobody ever comes around. Which I'm thankful for, but certainly glad it's you. So, tell me Kawmas, what is it that has you so bothered?'

Kawmas took a gulp from the pond. 'It's nothing. Really.'

Carwl looked in disgust at Kawmas with his single eye. 'You don't even believe that.'

Kawmas took another gulp. 'No, no I don't.'

'So out with it.'

'I'm just not sure about us.'

'We're just having a drink. Unless you're talking about a girl.'

'I don't mean any of that.'

Carwl took another drink. 'I see. You mean 'us' as in crows.'

'Yeah.'

'Who cares?'

'I do.'

'Well, you shouldn't. Everything in this world and that world get lumped into groups. Don't mean nothing. Me, I get up, eat, go to work and have a drink. My day ain't got nothing to do with anybody else.'

Kawmas looked down at the unlit pond and his reflection stared back up at him. He did care. He wasn't sure why.

'I get it Kawmas. I do.'

'What do you get?'

'That you look at me, that you look at every other crow, that you look at yourself and ask, am I just like them?'

‘And I shouldn’t care?’

‘Nope,’ Carwl said without hesitation.

‘Why not?’

‘Because life’s short enough as it is.’

There was a crack in the distance as though thunder had stomped on the sky, although in this case it was only the wind.

‘That pond is not a bar,’ declared a raven crossly as it touched down on the opposite side of the pond. The raven resembled a burly soldier as it stood upright, chest puffed out, wings tucked tightly against its side.

‘Shut it, raven,’ Carwl said with a hissing caw.

‘That wasn’t a request,’ the raven replied.

‘Neither was mine,’ Carwl hissed again.

‘Maybe we should go Carwl,’ pleaded Kawmas.

‘No. He should. I’ve done my work for the day. If I want to drink from the pond, I will.’

‘That’s where you’re wrong, crow. Your job isn’t done.’

‘Excuse me?’

‘Damn crows. You think you’re not kept track of? Crows want to move in on our job, you’d better believe we’re going to make sure you do your job.’

‘Screw you,’ Carwl cawed and shot over the pond at the raven.

Kawmas didn’t want to get involved. He wanted to deliver the pick. Kawmas wasn’t one to be involved with petty quarrels but Carwl was fighting a raven. And Carwl was a crow.

Screw the ravens!

The crows and the raven fought until a sudden boom split the air and water spilled out from the pond. The birds stopped and stared at the interloper; an enormous owl. Its wings seemed to span the length of the pond and it glared down at both the crows and the raven. It didn’t matter what world they crossed paths on, ravens and crows knew not to cross the owl.

Without a word, just a scolding glance, the raven took flight in the opposite direction, away from the monstrous bird sitting across the pond. Kawmas stared in awe for the owl seemed almost as large as the pond. He'd seen plenty owls in the world of life and they were always terrifying to behold but this was the first time he'd seen one in the life after. Somehow it seemed even more massive and more terrifying with the glowing globes of its eyes condemning him.

'Kawmas,' Carwl said. 'Real sorry about this.' And then Carwl was gone, leaving Kawmas alone as he gazed at the beast. His heart thumped while his mind flipped through visions of his life. And then he thought about the pick. There it was, floating on the pond.

Kawmas glanced at the owl and then darted for the pick. To his confusion, the owl did not attempt to stop him. He snatched the pick with his feet and flew through the blackness for a long time, almost as long as it took for his heart to cease its feverish beat and he saw the pick beating in the same way.

His heart continued to pound as he flew, constantly squeezing his feet to make sure the pick was still in his possession. Kawmas also did his best to juggle watching for owls and ravens and avoiding other crows, while he also looked for the man's father. He'd know him when he saw him for he'd glow - as would the pick - when they were in proximity to one another.

After a long time flying and searching, fatigue began to weigh the crow down. It was then he heard a guitar being strummed with care. The pick glowed.

'Hello' said Kawmas flying down to the man who was playing the guitar under a tree. He wasn't allowed to speak to the walkers in the living world. In the dead world though, it was entirely acceptable. The walkers of the living world weren't allowed to know that crows could speak. He wasn't sure why that was.

'Uh, hi,' said the guitarist. He stopped plucking chords and straightened himself up. He was a middle-aged man, though his long hair had grayed. His blue eyes seemed to sparkle as he glowed a faint white.

'I have a gift for you,' Kawmas said as he shuffled his feet around and pushed the pick forward. 'From your son.'

‘From my son,’ the man repeated, reaching for the pick with a shaking hand.

‘He wanted you to have this. Said wherever you were you probably needed one. And he wanted you to know he needs you, misses you and loves you.’

The man held the pick tightly in his hand, pressed it against his chest and closed his eyes. ‘Thank you,’ he said. ‘Thank you for bringing me this.’

The crow never quite understood this attachment to small inanimate objects. But he did understand the smile that overcame the man as he looked up through the walls of the dead world. While Kawmas was unable to smile, he felt it on the inside. It didn’t matter what led to its creation, just that it was. And while it would be fleeting, for the moment he had helped someone and had proven himself to be more than the pieces from his past.

And for today that was enough.

Mythological Context: Crows

In ancient, pre-Christian times, many cultures held the belief that birds acted as a kind of intermediary for people to connect with the Otherworld, probably because of their ability to attain the realms that humans could see but could not reach (the Heavens).

As with mythology in other cultures – for example, the Greek God Zeus transforming into a swan – Celtic deities or other talented individuals could also shapeshift to take on the appearance of birds. In Celtic Mythology, some of the most well-known examples include Tuán mac Cairill and the great seer Fionntan, both of whom took the form of eagles; Aonghus, who took the form of a swan; and Derbforgaill, also in the form of a swan when Cú Chulainn brought her down from the skies. The remaining literature also has a number of references to the druids making divinations based on their interpretation of the flight of birds or the cries of the raven.

Because of its conspicuous and somewhat menacing appearance, crows, ravens, and even magpies are believed to have taken on some of the darker aspects of that association with the Otherworld. This darker view was no doubt exacerbated by the fact that, as predators and scavengers, the birds would have been conspicuous feeding on carrion and, after a battle, on the corpses of the dead. Originally, the presence of these dark birds would have been associated with the land goddess fulfilling the natural order or the recurring cycle of nature i.e. the land – through the land goddess – was reclaiming what had originally been produced from it.

Over time however, and with the coming of Christianity, those interpretations were diluted and changed. The later, medieval writers took a much grimmer view of those native beliefs, portraying the crows as representative of a land goddess who obtained a perverse pleasure from battle carnage and the slaughter of humankind.

The most frequently portrayed in this manner was Badhbh, a manifestation of the triplicated mother goddess, Danu. In the literature from early medieval times, Badhbh is depicted as a cruel war goddess who appears in the form of a scaldcrow to announce the death of heroic warriors and other figures. Hovering around the battlefield or flying above the fighting armies, she's also depicted as releasing terrifying shrieks, taking a kind of demonic pleasure from the enormous loss of life.

It's because of this portrayal that we find one of Celtic mythology's most striking images in the medieval account of the death of Cú Chulainn. In that story, although he is dying, the fierce warrior straps himself to a standing stone so that he can remain upright to combat his enemies. Fearful of his great fighting skill, the opposing warriors refrain from approaching him until a carrion crow descends to perch on the stone above his head, a clear signal that the great hero has died.

Traces of these negative aspects of crows and other dark birds continued in local folklore and literature up to relatively recent times and ravens and hooded crows were often seen as a bad omen or a sign of potential misfortune. When a number of birds (a 'murder' of crows) were observed hovering or squawking near a house, it was often seen as a dark portent that prophesied the death of a member of the household. When a solitary crow was observed acting unusually in a field, there was also a folk belief that the bird represented an aspect of an Otherworld figure or a grievous sinner who hadn't been able to 'move on' after his death.

Vestiges of the prophetic association with certain birds such as crows remain in contemporary society through the use of children's rhymes such as "One for sorrow, two for joy …" used in some places for crows as well as for magpies. Crows and ravens, meanwhile, continue to be used liberally in film, books and other media as symbols or metaphors for the occult.

Some things never change.

Brian O'Sullivan

The Cut

Brian O'Sullivan

A little glossary:
Cruit – an old stringed instrument
Draoi – a druid
Galar rúin – an illness caused by holding a terrible secret
Labhraidh – an old Irish name (pronounced 'Lowry' in English)
Léine – a short-like garment
Na Laighin – A tribe based around the Irish east coast
Rí – The Irish (Gaelic) word for 'chieftain'. Ireland didn't really have 'kings', in the English sense of the word.

When the mother and son came to see him, Labhraidh Loingseach, rí of Na Laighin, was sitting at his favourite seat on the riverbank, attended by the cruit-player, Craiftine. Spotting them in the distance, he frowned and held up one hand to silence the prattling musician.

Labhraidh looked at the woman. She looked at him.

'We'll continue this discussion later,' he said dismissing his friend.

Craiftine, knowing from experience when it was pointless to argue, sighed and rose to his feet. Making his way downriver, he smiled amiably at the two newcomers for they were known to him, neighbours of his family at Carnan. The woman, for her part, smiled in return as she dismissed the boy, sending him down to the river's edge to throw stones at the passing water.

Labhraidh Loingseach sat back on the low boulder he was using as a seat and regarded the approaching figure. With thirty-eight years on him, the *rí* was an impressive figure with a warrior physique hardened by years of battle. His face still bore the trace of those combats: a broken nose, a scar down one cheek, another across his forehead. Despite such brutal traits however, his features were softened by the thoughtful eyes of long-held leadership and a long mane of brown hair that fell to his shoulders.

'I see you Sorcha Uí Uilleann,' he called to the approaching woman.

Affecting nonchalance, the woman avoided his gaze by focussing on the act of brushing dirt from her *léine*. It was only as she sat, taking a position on the boulder alongside him, that she returned the ritual greeting.

'I see you Labhraidh Loingseach.'

Both stared out at the passing waters of the river in silence before speaking again.

'Labhraidh Moen, Labhraidh Lorc. It's been a long time. So very long.' Sorcha smiled a smile that lit up her face. She brushed a loose strand of hair from her forehead, revealing one or two white strands against the raven darkness that only served to accentuate her beauty.

Labhraidh unconsciously lifted one hand to brush the hair back from his own forehead but paused in mid-movement and dropped it instead to grasp a nearby cup of water.

'It may have been a long time but the whispers of your beauty have proven true. The passing of years has treated you kindly and done nothing to wither your bloom.'

She laughed at that. 'And what else did those whispers tell you?'

He drank deep from the goblet before answering. 'They may have mentioned your family's return to Laighin lands at Carnan three years past.'

'And you never thought to visit?'

Labhraidh shifted awkwardly on his seat but then laughed at his own discomfort. 'The wounds of the heart heal more slowly than the wounds of the flesh, dear one. When you took Conall as your man, the cut was deep. I had no call to resent your choice of course, nevertheless …'. He shrugged.

'Rest easy, Labhraidh Loingseach. Our parting was bitter but with age I've come to understand my own selfishness in the matter.' She held up a hand to still his response. 'We shared affection and closeness but I understand now you were only doing what you were driven to do and I cannot begrudge you for being yourself. You had a need to reclaim the position of *rí*, to lead the tribe and rule the land. I cannot fault you for we had more than our fill of good times. It pleases me to delve into those memories and examine from time to time. I have no regrets.'

Labhraidh turned away to toss a twig into the river. He watched it strike the water where the hungry current immediately snatched it up and whipped it away.

'The whispers also told of how your man died of fever.'

Sorcha grew silent and thoughtful, allowing herself the pain of memory. 'It was a hard death,' she admitted at last. 'It took him five days to die, five days of pain, of sweating fever and choking for breath. On the fifth night, he died and although his passing brought grief, it also brought relief.'

'My sympathy to you. Conall and I had friendship from old times, the fighting times. I know he was a good man.'

She nodded. 'He was.'

'And he left you with land.'

'He did.'

'And a son.'

She paused and looked at the ground. 'Yes.'

With that Labhraidh chuckled softly, causing the woman to regard him with a frown.

'Why do you laugh?'

'Forgive me, Sorcha. It's not to mock that loss. It's just …'. He hesitated, 'I recognised an old trait of yours, the habit of falling back on the least flowered of language when you're tense or upset. To see that again after all these years …'.

He coughed and gestured helplessly.

'But it's not to reminisce old days that you've travelled all the way from Carnan, is it Sorcha?'

'No,' the woman admitted. 'It wasn't my intent to bandy words with you but sitting here together stirs memories … Memories I hadn't expected of simpler, happier, times. It was pleasant to lose myself to the past, just for a moment at least and …'. She sighed and her posture straightened. 'I've come to speak with you about my son, Labhraidh. Flann is the name he carries and I'd seek a boon of you on his behalf.'

'Of course.' The *rí* of Na Laighin made an easy gesture as he looked over to where the boy, a handsome youth of fifteen years or so, was wading in a minor inlet poking the riverbed with a stick to stir up hidden trout. 'He looks a fine youth. You wish him taught in the warrior path? Have him placed in the …?

'He's been selected for The Cut.'

Labhraidh stiffened. 'Oh,' he said, glancing sideways at her before returning his gaze to the river once more.

'Did you do this to punish me, Labhraidh? For daring to leave you sixteen years ago? Everyone knows the fierce vengeance of Labhraidh Lorc.'

'To punish you? Of course not. It's …'. The *rí* sighed. 'You know The Cut is a sacred ritual. That is why our *draoi* selects the barber. I have no say in who they choose for the role.'

'They say it was you who instigated The Cut in the first place,' she countered. 'And besides, you have a say in whether they live or die.'

He looked at her with new hostility. 'What do you mean?'

'The people have noticed Labhraidh.'

'What have they noticed?'

'The fact that all those who serve as your groomsman on the day of The Cut are mysteriously short-lived. Over all those years, how many of the youths who tended to your grooming remain alive today?'

Labhraidh made no answer and the silence lay between them like a stone.

'None,' continued Sorcha at last.' None of them live. Every one of them died suddenly or disappeared shortly after serving you.' She paused. 'Did you truly believe people would not notice?'

The *rí* regarded her closely. 'And people speak openly of this?'

She nodded. 'Behind closed doors such talk is common. The talk's hardly one of revolt or revulsion for none forget your vengeance on your uncle. In truth, you're well liked. Everyone knows your reign has brought peace and prosperity.'

Labhraidh grunted, clearly uncomfortable, and she latched onto that discomfort to plead her case. 'Do not kill my son, Labhraidh. I have lost one most dear to me. My heart will not survive the loss of another.'

'The selection for The Cut is not mine, Sorcha.'

Upset now, the woman got to her feet. 'I have never asked you for anything Labhraidh Loingseach but I ask you now for this.' She made as though to walk away but then paused and faced him again. 'One thing you should consider, Labhraidh. I left Carnan and your company sixteen years ago. My son has sixteen years on him. Reflect on that when you make your choice.'

With a swirl of her cloak, Sorcha Uí Uilleann departed, stalking furiously downriver.

Stunned by the parting shot, Labhraidh stared after her in wonder.

***

On the day of The Cut, Flann nervously approached the settlement of Bearna, a cluster of huts and a longhouse set on a small rise close by the Liffey river. After two weeks of instruction and cleansing for the ritual of grooming, the Laighin *rí* felt well-versed in his responsibilities, if somewhat uneasy.

Having identified himself to a warrior patrolling the settlement's perimeter, Flann was escorted into the longhouse where the *rí* sat in conversation with his bodyguard, the warrior Connla.

'It's the groomsman,' the guard announced. Connla, an ugly, squat man with facial tattoos and a black beard, glanced curiously at the newcomer before turning his gaze back to his leader. Labhraidh however, was already staring hard at the youth, struggling to find a familiar line in the contours of his face. In this he was frustrated, for the youth's features were dominated by his mother's influence. With a grunt the *rí* slumped back in his chair.

Taking their cue, Connla and the warrior departed the longhouse. Labhraidh waited until the door had closed firmly behind them before gesturing towards the nearby table where a bronze razor had been laid out on a flat stone. Prepared by the *draoi's* teaching, the youth knew what to do and although his hand was trembling he reached out to take the razor up, slashing it once or twice through the air to get the feel of it. Although it was small, the blade was thin and extremely sharp, perfect for cutting through thick strands of hair.

Noting how much the youth was trembling, that the *rí* felt compelled to stand up, reach over and take the instrument from him. Flann stood shaking before him, his eyes looking down at the ground.

'You know the responsibility of the task assigned to you?' asked Labhraidh.

'To groom you. To shave your noble chin and groom the great mane of hair.' The youth answered without hesitation, repeating the phrasing he'd been taught by the druid, a phrase that had become so ritualised most people could recite the words perfectly from memory.

Labhraidh grunted as he regained his seat.

'Then let us make a start of it.'

Despite his fear, Flann moved to stand behind the *rí's* chair and started on his hair. Despite his nervousness, he managed to still his trembling hand as he focussed on the task before him. Labhraidh meanwhile, sat patiently as the first strand was cut away and placed in a bronze bowl which would later be symbolically put to the flame. He bore the youth's rough grooming with forbearance, even forgave the nick in his cheek where the edge of the razor pricked him as Flann worked on his moustache and beard.

For a time, there was silence in the roundhouse, underlined by the low crackle of the firepit and the occasional *snick* of the razor blade slicing through a particularly thick strand of hair, the locks fluttering down to curl in the bowl on the hard-packed earth floor. A small pile had already gathered beneath the *rí's* stool when the expected exclamation finally came. From the corner of his eye, Labhraidh saw the youth's razor hand freeze in place, heard him take one shocked step back from the *rí*.

'Boy,' he said. For a moment there was no response. 'Boy,' he repeated, more angrily this time. 'Tell me what you see.'

The youth's voice, when it came, was tight and frightened. 'Your ears.'

'Yes?'

'Your ears are long and leathered. And coated with hair. You have ... You have the ears of a horse.'

With startling alacrity, the *rí* swung up from his seat and rounded on the boy who, startled, backed away in alarm, too frightened to even attempt to use the razor to defend himself. Labhraidh placed one strong hand against his chest, pinning him against the wall of the longhouse.

'So now you know my secret.'

Flann nodded dumbly.

'A secret you'll never share with any living person.'

The youth shook his head desperately.

'Swear it!'

'I swear!'

'The full vow. Swear it on your mother's head.'

'I swear. I'll never share your secret with any living person. Upon my mother's head I swear.'

Labhraidh held Flann in place, staring into his eyes with furious intent until assured the youth understood the consequences of his actions.

'Good. You are now *faoi gheas* – under sacred obligation. Do not forget that for should you break this hallowed oath there will be no saving you. Your corpse will join that of your mother's in the darkest hole of the forest, gnawed on by the foxes and the wild creatures.'

Finally, releasing him, Labhraidh returned to his seat. Hearing no sound of movement from the terrified youth, he turned about and gave his sharpest scowl.

'Oath or not, boy! You still have work to do. Complete your task but leave enough to cover the ears or you'll suffer the consequences.'

***

It was noon the following day before Flann returned to his mother's holding in the hills of Carnan. Sorcha Uí Uilleann had been seated on a viewpoint overlooking the western trail since the afternoon of the previous day. Finally, seeing the familiar shape arrive up the valley, a great relief washed over her and she fell to her knees with tears of gratitude.

Much good to you, Labhraidh Loingseach. There's some trace of the man I knew in you yet.

By the time, her son had climbed the hill trail and worked his way to where she stood waiting, she'd cried her heart out and dried her eyes, and their reunion was one of joy. At supper that night however, Flann was moody and withdrawn and went to bed early. Over the following days, a great lassitude came over him and by the time the next moon came around he was a shade of the handsome youth he'd been. On those occasions Sorcha dared seek the reason behind his deterioration, the youth rounded on her with uncharacteristic vehemence, his body tight and locked with stress.

One morning, Flann remained abed, complaining of aches to his neck and shoulders. By evening that same day, the pain had spread to his chest and his legs. Fearing the worst, Sorcha dispatched a servant to fetch the healer Dathal, a cousin of hers whom she'd helped in the past and who she knew would not refuse her. An old man, it took Dathal several days to make the trip to Carnan and by the time he arrived, Flann lay in a sweating fever.

Greeting his cousin, the healer immediately sought his patient, examining the youth's body and drawing the answers to the questions he asked in a low, gentle voice. It was some time before he emerged from the roundhouse to where his cousin was waiting fretfully.

'Well?' she demanded.

'Your son has a *galar rúin*.'

Sorcha shook her head in a mixture of confusion and dismay. A *galar rúin*. She'd heard the term once before and vaguely recalled it referred to a black secret that poisoned one's sleep and waking hours. She'd never encountered anyone who'd ever suffered from it and had always believed it an old gossip tale.

Seeing her confusion, the healer clarified further. 'Flann carries a burden, cousin. A secret he won't share, and which threatens to eat him up from the inside. If it's not dealt to, it'll get worse and he'll wither away.' He paused then and grew quiet, regretting the fact of having to deliver such bad news.

'What can we do to save him?' Sorcha demanded. 'How can we treat the *galar rúin* and bring my boy back to health?'

'We can do nothing.'

'You'd better explain yourself,' she told him harshly.

'Your son has to do it himself.'

The woman looked from the healer to her son and back again. 'Flann's as weak as a new-born,' she exclaimed. 'How can you expect him to do anything?'

'The secret he carries has to be expelled before it kills him. Only Flann can do that. When I questioned him, I did so in a way that allowed him to admit the truth behind my suspicions but he revealed that he could tell no other living person.'

Sorcha shrivelled up in grief. 'He will not do that. Whatever secret he carries, he will carry to his grave.'

The healer thought about that. 'I have an idea,' he said at last. 'This is what we'll do.'

***

The following morning at dawn, Dathal helped Sorcha take her son into the forest. By then Flann could barely walk upright and had to be carried, supported between the two of them. Moving through the forest, they eventually reached a clearing with a young oak tree at its centre. Beside the tree a small spring-fed pool gleamed bright in the morning sun.

Seating Flann by the tree and arranging him with his back against the trunk, the healer explained the situation.

'You have a *galar rúin*, Flann. A black secret so big and so bad it's jammed you up inside and making you sick. If you don't deal to it, it'll wither you away.'

Too upset to say anything, the boy simply nodded. The healer placed a reassuring hand on the boy's shoulder.

'The only way to cure a bad secret is to release it. I know you're *faoi gheas* not to tell a living person but you might still release it by telling another living entity instead.'

He pointed to a bole hole on the eastern side of the trunk, at a height level with the youth's head. 'When you're ready, place your lips as close to that bole hole as you can and then whisper these words into it:

Is duitse táim á innsint
A phuill an chrainn,
A phuill an chrainn

'After that, tell the tree the secret you've been holding inside you. Whisper it out of you and into the tree and it'll keep your secret safe. If you don't think you have the right of it the first time, just go through it again. Repeat it as many times as you have to until you've told the tree everything.'

With that, Dathal and Sorcha retreated into the forest and found a sunny spot by a stream where they waited in anxious silence, the Carnan woman wringing her hands in despair.

Finally, when Dathal felt it was time, they returned to the clearing and there they found Flann still as weak as when they'd left him but with the pallor now faded from his face. Seeing the fresh colours swarm his features, Sorcha rushed towards him, weeping with relief.

As she hugged her son close, she stared up at the tree, wondering what secrets it now contained.

***

It was almost a full year later that the musician Craiftine again passed through the land of Carnan where, after spending time with his family, he also partook of Sorcha Uí Uilleann's hospitality. After a feast of welcome, Sorcha invited him to provide them with entertainment and getting to his feet, the musician bowed gracefully, answering. 'For the warm welcome I've received I will happily play.'

Pulling his cruit free, Craiftine rested the instrument's wooden base across his chest, raised the bow and started to play, his deep voice chanting in perfect harmony to the droning chords he drew from the instrument.

Following the applause at the termination of his first song, he commenced another only to have it abruptly curtailed when the neck of the instrument unexpectedly snapped in two. Examining the broken section that dangled from the network of strings, the musician fingered the exposed grain of wood with his finger. 'I shouldn't complain,' he said at last. 'There was always a weak joint in that neck threatening to snap. There's no surprise it finally fulfilled its promise.'

Nevertheless, he frowned in vexation.

'And yet, with Samhain almost on us I'll need a new instrument, for Labhraidh Loingseach would have me play the feasting he holds at Bearna.'

Sorcha, who still bore Labhraidh great goodwill for the sparing of her son, was happy to offer what assistance she could. 'There's no shortage of trees for you to choose in the forest, Craiftine. Take whatever wood you need to make your instrument and welcome.'

'Aaah, but for the perfect instrument I'll need to find the perfect tree that will play its heart for me.'

Sorcha, who was ever more pragmatist than artist, answered the musician's fastidiousness with a shrug. 'I'm sure you'll find a tree to your satisfaction in the forests of Carnan.'

And so it was that the following day, Craiftine found himself in the same clearing where Flann had told his secret to the oak tree. Staring at that very tree, it seemed to the musician that it was almost leaning forward towards him in eagerness to serve.

You're a willing tree, he thought as he pulled an axe from his bag. After cutting a substantial branch from the oak, he returned to Bearna where he fashioned a new instrument.

***

Several days later and bearing his new cruit, Craiftine attended the great feast of Bearna where several hundred people were already gathered for the festivities. An important celebration, the feast was also used by the canny *rí* as an opportunity to reward trusted comrades, to initiate the establishment of new alliances and to enhance his reputation for generosity among the people of his tribe.

When Craiftine arrived, the longhouse was black with people and he struggled to find a seat in the corner where he could use the walls to best effect to reflect and amplify his music. Seeing his friend, Labhraidh sidled up beside him to clap a hand on his shoulder. 'Play well tonight, Craiftine. I have important guests and it'd do well if your music put them in happy space of mind.'

Calling the crowd to silence. The *rí* directed their attention to the corner where the musician was already producing a few chords to test the sound. Taking a deep breath, he closed his eyes and began to play.

The first chords he plucked hung in the air for several heartbeats, lingering like a haunted silence before they finally dissipated. The crowd sat entranced, eyes widening at the musician's skill as he broke into a faster tune with a rushing tempo, fingers flicking over the strings so fast they appeared as a blur. The cruit responded like no other instrument Craiftine had ever played before, the notes resonating with an Otherworldly hum. As the tune slipped into an even faster progression however, he began to wonder, for the instrument seemed to be taking on a life of its own, producing sound a moment before his fingers even plucked the strings. Open-mouthed, the crowd stared, somehow sensing that the music was too powerful for a single man and that something was amiss.

With growing concern, Craiftine realised that the instrument was now leading the tune and he tried desperately to keep up as it rang out a cadence of its own, a pounding, oddly distinct rhythm that sounded so clear it resembled a pattern of syllables or the eerie chorus of a song. Drawn along by the power of the music, Craiftine sounded out the words now being issued by the cruit:

Labhraidh Lorc has Horses Ears
Labhraidh Lorc has Horses Ears
Labhraidh Lorc has Horses Ears

With a surge of panic, Craiftine wrenched himself free of the cruit and desperately flung the instrument against the walls of the longhouse where it smashed into pieces. Horrified, he turned to stare at Labhraidh Loingseach but by then it was all too late. Many of the crowd were already standing, looking aghast from Craiftine to the white-faced Labhraidh and back again. Chairs and tables were overturned as others surged to their feet. Children cried, dogs barked and even the fire in the longhouse firepit seemed to take on a life of its own, blazing up like an inferno as the tribal members fled the longhouse.

***

It was afternoon of the following day when Labhraidh Loingseach, *rí* of Na Laighin, was sitting at his favourite seat on the riverbank in meeting with the cruit-player, Craiftine. Spotting the woman who was coming to see him, he frowned and held up one hand to silence the desperately apologetic musician.

'We'll continue this discussion later,' he said, dismissing his friend and Craiftine, relieved to depart with his head, rose to his feet and made his way downriver while the newcomer drew closer.

'I see you Sorcha Uí Uilleann,' he called to the approaching woman.

'I see you Labhraidh Loingseach.'

Sorcha sat down beside him and both stared out at the passing waters of the river in silence.

'You're here for Samhain,' the *rí* said at last.

'I am. Though I missed the festivities last night.'

'But you'll have heard what came to pass.'

'I have.' Sorcha bit her lip. 'They say you held up your hair so that all could see your blemish. That was brave.'

'I could hardly do otherwise. Sometimes the truth insists on speaking and last night was such an occasion. In all honestly, I'm pleased to no longer carry the burden.'

Sorcha nodded in sympathy. 'Can I see for myself?' she asked.

Labhraidh sighed but then turned his head to one side for her and lifted his mane, allowing her to see the hairy ear beneath.

Sorcha examined the ear with quiet fascination. 'You had no such blemish when we were together.'

'No. They started to change a little over a year after we separated. One healer – who oddly died the next day – told me that it was a natural illness but I've often wondered whether it had something to do with the terms of our parting. I've had few happy days since.'

'You succeeded in retaining your chieftainship. That's a happy outcome.'

'Perhaps.' Labhraidh shook his head slowly as though in wonder at how events had turned out. 'All our lives we're told no chieftain with a blemish will ever rule and yet the morning after my own, most morbid of blemishes is revealed, the tribal council tell me they do not care.'

'You may recall how I once told you that you were well liked. For a ferocious warrior, your leadership brought a peace and prosperity the people are reluctant to give up. Blemish or no, I suspect your leadership will remain unchallenged for some time to come.'

Labhraidh snorted and withdrew into silence. It was some time before he spoke again. 'Sorcha,' he said at last, his face still turned away from her. 'Flann is not my son.'

The words were more statement than question but now it was the Carnan woman's turn to sigh.

'It's I who sits shamed, Labhraidh. I regret those words for Flann is Conall's offspring. I feel no joy at my deception but I feared for my son. I hope you can forgive me.'

The *rí* of Na Laighin waved her concerns away. 'Your pale lie fades against the darkness of my own deeds, dear one.'

Both lapsed into silence, watching the smooth rapids endlessly whipping by.

'What will you do now, Labhraidh?' Sorcha asked at last.

'I will continue in the role of chieftain. Apparently, that is what the people want.' He paused. 'But first there's the question of Craiftine's tree. I would dearly like to visit Carnan and hear for myself what other secrets it contains.'

'When in Carnan,' suggested Sorcha. 'Perhaps you'll accept my hospitality.'

Labhraidh gave a wry smile then reached over to take her hand in his.

'Perhaps, I will,' he said.

Mythological Context: Labhraidh Loingseach

Labhraidh (pronounced 'Lowry' in English – that's actually where the English name comes from) was a mythical chieftain and a founding ancestor of Na Laighin – a major tribe based in Ireland's south-east. The sobriquet 'Loingseach' means 'The exiled one' but in the ancient literature he's often referred to with the sobriquet 'Moen', which means 'dumb' or 'Lorc' which mean 'fierce'. For that reason, this character often appears under the name Labhraidh Moen or Labhraidh Lorc instead (nothing like keeping it simple!).

There are actually several variations to the story of how Labhraidh got his name but nearly all of them involve him being mute as a child (hence, called Moen). In some variants, this situation resulted from seeing his father violently murdered by his uncle, Cobhthach. The most well-known story tells how Moen was playing hurling on a field when he was struck on the shin, causing caused him to cry out in pain "I'm hurt!'. When the other players heard him speak, they were so surprised, they declared *"Labhraigh Moen!"* (The Dumb One speaks) and the name stuck.

Some years later, when Cobhthach asked the people who the most generous nobleman in Ireland was (naturally expecting it to be himself) they all answered 'Labhraidh'. Jealous, the king had his nephew banished overseas where he established a settlement somewhere along the English channel. Several years later, the exiled Labhraidh returned to Ireland with a force of over two thousand foreigners, all bearing a distinctive broad spear (**co laighnibh**).

Defeating and killing his uncle in battle, Labhraidh offered his army land in the Leinster region and because of their spears, they subsequently became known as the Laighin – Na Laighin.

Because of the lingering impacts of English colonisation (even centuries later), most Irish people aren't familiar with the stories of

Labhraidh apart from the story of the 'Horses Ears' which has been pushed as a child's fairy-tale in Ireland since the 17th century. This story actually dates from the 10th century and is believed to have been adapted from a tale about King Midas that was popular in Medieval Europe at the time (and in particular from a Welsh variation of the Midas tale involving the character March ap Meirchion). Down in West Cork – where I'm from – the variation of the story I grew up with was based around an O'Driscoll castle on an island in Lough Hyne.

It's always saddened me that so many Irish people are unfamiliar with their own history/mythology and this story came about as an attempt to bring some of the real character of Labhraigh Loingseach back into contemporary form, to lift his story from the dubious status of children's entertainment. This version of the story fits correctly within the established mythology but note that the relationship between Labhraidh and Sorcha is pure invention on my part. The cultural concept of the **galar rúnach** was a far later development but works well in terms of the 'secret' aspect of the story. Although the concept is explained more fully in the book Beara Dark Legends, it does not have any real connection to the earliest development of the story.

Brian O'Sullivan

The Authors

Donna Rutherford

Originally from Scotland, Donna now lives by the beach in New Zealand's South Island. She is a mother of four children, a secondary school teacher and a long-distance runner. Her writing is inspired by the bonds of family, connection to our lands, and the journeys we make from one life to another.

Donna has written two novels under the pen name Ruthie Morgan. Her first novel of fiction – *Skylark* - was shortlisted for the Impress Prize 2015, made finalist in the Readers Favourite International Book Awards 2015. Was the recipient of the B.R.A.G. Medallion 2015 (US. Book Readers Appreciation Group) and won the Drunken Druid Book of the Year 2014 – an Irish award for independent authors and small press publisher's books.

The sequel to Skylark – *Borrowed Wings* was published in 2016. Ruthie's third novel – *From Where We Came* – is due to be published late 2018.

Damien J Howard

Damien was born and raised in Dublin on a healthy dose of old Irish tales from his mother's Tipperary upbringing and his father's travels at sea across the entire world.

From tales of the Headless Horseman of Templemore to wild bets in dodgy tattoo parlours in Mozambique, Damien fell in love with stories at a very early age and now is trying his hand at telling them.

Jerry Vandal

Born, raised and still residing in Cleveland, Ohio, Jerry W. Vandal grew up on a diet of Ninja Turtles, X-Men and Final Fantasy. Having spent much of his teenage years drawing dragons, caped (and non-caped) vigilantes, and mutants, he also started putting together stories in his head. While obtaining degrees in English and Psychology from Cleveland State University, he began working on crafting those stories with words. Presently he works with kids who have Autism and has seen publication through Gray Haven Comics.

He is an avid reader of comic books, lover of mythology and make-believe worlds.

Brian O'Sullivan

Brian O'Sullivan was born in county Cork, Ireland. Completing a degree at University College Cork, he went on to travel extensively but now resides in New Zealand, running Irish Imbas Books with his partner and family in Wellington. Brian writes regular articles on Irish folklore and mythology, aspects of Irish culture and his own writing at his blog on the Irish Imbas Books website.

Brian mostly writes fiction that incorporates strong elements of Irish culture, language, history and mythology. These include literary short stories (The Irish Muse collection), mystery thrillers (The Beara Trilogy) and a bestselling contemporary version of the Fionn mac Cumhaill/ Fenian legends (The Fionn mac Cumhaill Series). He also has a number of non-fiction books on the go.

The Celtic Mythology Short Story Competition

The **Celtic Mythology Short Story Competition** is an initiative established by Irish Imbas Books to promote the writing of contemporary Celtic culture-based stories and to encourage a more accurate understanding of the Celtic cultures and Celtic mythology.

This book, the **Irish Imbas: Celtic Mythology Short Story Collection 2018** is the third output from this initiative. It's hoped to repeat the competition and the publication of appropriate stories on an annual basis.

Full details for this competition can be found at the Irish Imbas Books website irishimbasbooks.com

Prizes: include:

First Prize: $500 and story published in the next Irish Imbas Celtic Mythology Collection
Second prize: $250 and story published in the next Irish Imbas Celtic Mythology Collection
Third prize: $100 and story published in the next Irish Imbas Celtic Mythology Collection

Any kind of fiction short story can generally be submitted (action, romance, drama, humour etc.) however they are judged against the following criteria:

- Celtic mythology forms a fundamental element of the story (i.e. the characters can be characters from Celtic mythology, the action can take place in a mythological location, mythological concepts can be used etc.)
- Any Celtic folklore or mythological reference used in the story is as authentic and as correct as possible

- The story has a compelling theme, engaging characters, a credible setting and a convincing storyline.

Submissions for the next competition will be accepted **from September 2018**. Conditions may change so please check the Irish Imbas Books website for details.

If you'd like to receive our monthly newsletter on future books and audio (some not available through the larger ebook stores), elements of Irish mythology, folklore, culture and the creative process we use, please feel free to sign up at the Irish Imbas Books website.

Other Books from Irish Imbas Books:

If you liked the style and content of the Celtic Mythology Collection Series, why not try **Fionn: The Stalking Silence** – available FREE at the Irish Imbas Books site and at all good ebook stores.

Ireland 192 AD:

In dark mid-winter a pregnant refugee travels through the wilderness to the safety of a distant settlement. Alone and stalked by a relentless predator, she has to draw on all her courage and cunning to survive.

A sample of what the reviewers say:

"Even knowing the story outline (from the myth/history) I was caught. Wonderfully lyric prose, it seems a fitting entry into the world of "Fionn mac Cumhaill."

"A short but tense tale of a pregnant woman in ancient Ireland fighting to survive an encounter with a starving wolf."

"An incredibly tense and satisfying read about the face-off between a predator and a lone pregnant woman in the wilderness of ancient Ireland."

Fionn: Defence of Ráth Bládhma:

[The Fionn mac Cumhaill Series: Book 1]

Irish Bestseller and SPFBO Competition 2016 Finalist

Ireland: 192 A.D. A time of strife and treachery. Political ambition and inter-tribal conflict has set the country on edge, testing the strength of long-established alliances.

Following their victory at the battle of Cnucha, Clann Morna are hungry for power. Meanwhile, a mysterious war party roams the 'Great Wild' and a ruthless magician is intent on murder.

In the secluded valley of Glenn Ceoch, disgraced druidess Bodhmhall and the woman warrior Liath Luachra have successfully avoided the bloodshed for many years. Now, the arrival of a pregnant refugee threatens the peace they have created together. The odds are overwhelming and death stalks on every side.

Based on the ancient Irish Fenian Cycle texts, the bestselling Fionn mac Cumhaill Series recounts the fascinating and pulse-pounding tale of the birth and adventures of Ireland's greatest hero, Fionn mac Cumhaill.

The most **authentic** and **entertaining** Irish mythological adventure/fantasy series on the market, this book includes the following **extra content**:

- a glossary with explanations of ancient Irish cultural concepts
- historical notes on the Fenian Cycle
- a pronunciation guide and links to an online audio pronunciation guide

A sample of what the reviewers say:

"I loved this book. It's a very mature and culturally rich interpretation, a far cry from some of the Celtic pop literature that is around today. Well written and captivating, with a fair dollop of grit and wit. Strong characters, great development, excellent story telling. Worth more than the price of a coffee."

An Ireland of centuries ago, threaded through with myth and magic, but very 'real' for all that. Dark and at times violent, it is balanced by affirming friendships and relationships, and a very strong female cast."

"If you're sick of elves, chivalrous knights and arcane quests like me, this is probably the most exciting and refreshing book you'll read in a long time. Five stars!"

"Powerful female characters are all too rare in literature. The druidess Bodhmhall, and her lover the warrior Liath Luachra will inspire current and

future generations of women. O'Sullivan keeps a cracking pace in this, the first of his Fionn mac Cumhaill series.'

Review from 'Bookworm Blues' Speculative Fiction/Fantasy Review Blog

"You know how some books come out of left field and just shock you? Well, this was one of those. If you're looking for an action/adventure fantasy that is different than the normal, look no further. This book has some welcome diversity, and a story that is absolutely unforgiving. This is a novel based on some ancient Irish text, and is full of myth and magic and I just loved it for that. The writing is tight and the book is well edited. I welcomed the strong female characters, the obvious twist on tropes, and the way the author genuinely owned the book he wrote."

Review from 'The Qwillery' Book Review Blog

"The characters were well developed, the plot was gripping and the characters were both realistic and interesting. It was however, the prose that really made this book. It was so very well written.
Hats off to Brian O'Sullivan for telling this myth in a truly evocative way."

Review from Bibliotropic' Book Review Blog

"It leaves you feeling like you really know the land and its people when you finish the last page. You can practically smell the livestock of the settlement, feel the chill in the air, expect to hear certain voices from the distance. Even if you're not captivated by the story itself, you're taken in by the setting and the way it comes alive."

Beara: Dark Legends

[The Beara Trilogy – Book 1]

Nobody knows much about reclusive historian Muiris (Mos) O'Súilleabháin except that he doesn't share his secrets freely. Mos, however, has a *"sixth sense for history, a unique talent for finding lost things"*.

Lured from seclusion, despite his own misgivings, Mos is hired to locate the final resting place of legendary Irish hero, Fionn mac Cumhaill. Confronted by a thousand–year old mystery, the distractions of a beguiling circus performer and a ruthlessly lethal competitor, Mos must draw on his knowledge of Gaelic lore to defy his enemies and survive his own family history in Beara.

Beara: Dark Legends is the first in a trilogy of unforgettable Irish thrillers. Propulsive, atmospheric and darkly humorous, *Dark Legends* introduces an Irish hero like you've never seen before. Nothing you thought you knew about Ireland will ever be the same again.

A sample of what the reviewers say:

"A great tale with all the elements of a "Who dunnit" all woven into modern and ancient Irish history and mythology."

"Fantastic book - couldn't put it down. A 'MUST' read! original Irish thriller, historical novel, mystery novel, best book I've read in years."

"O'Sullivan has done an amazing job of introducing a culture that many would say is dying and using it as the basis for a unique and exciting thriller. I think I've learned more about Irish history and the Irish language in this one book than I have in many years of school and television, without it once feeling forced or jaded."

"A great mixture of a strong story and strong characters, dark (some very dark) themes and wonderfully evocative descriptions of the wild Irish landscape, interspersed with ancient Irish lore running throughout the book."

"Excellent story, very well thought out, many twists and turns that weren't expected. Thoroughly enjoyed the main character Mos and his no nonsense-take no crap attitude to life, he says what most of us often probably think but are too polite to say, highly entertaining!"

"O'Sullivan's cast of international characters enliven this tale of archaeological intrigue, magic, murder and sex, set mainly in West Cork, Ireland. Dual story lines, across different time zones, reveal secrets of Irish spirituality, ancient lore and language."

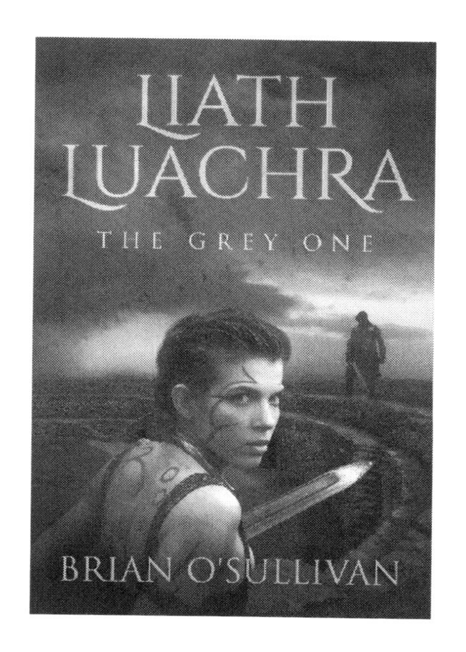

Liath Luachra: The Grey One

Ireland: 188 A.D. A land of tribal affiliations, secret alliances and treacherous rivalries.

The woman warrior Liath Luachra has survived two brutal years fighting with mercenary war party "The Friendly Ones" but now the winds are shifting. Dispatched on a murderous errand where nothing is as it seems, she must survive a group of treacherous comrades, the unwanted advances of her battle leader and a personal history that might be her own undoing.

Clanless and friendless, she can count on nothing but her wits, her fighting skills and her natural ferocity to see her through.

Woman warrior, survivor, killer and future guardian to Irish hero Fionn mac Cumhaill – this is her story.

A sample of what the reviewers say:

"In the legends of Fionn mac Cumhaill, Liath Luachra is an intriguing name with minimal context but in Brian O'Sullivan's adaptions she becomes a most

fascinating and formidable character in her own right. Her backstory is a great read; brigands and bloodshed, second-guessings and double-crossings. This is an Ancient Ireland that is entrancing and savage, much like Liath Luachra herself."

"I re-immersed myself in the very believable world the author creates and couldn't put the book down until I had finished it. It shed so much light on the character of Liath - her grim experiences and her strength in the face of adversity. I am now going back to reread the other books, which I am sure will be all the richer for a greater understanding of Liath. You don't often come across such a compelling hero(ine), written with such depth and understanding."

"This is a fast-paced traverse through bush trails and battles with a female heroine who is commanding and fascinating."

"As always, the plotting is riveting – full of twists and turns – and the action is full on, hell for leather. If you like Games of Thrones style dramas with a strong splash of Celtic culture, this is a book you'll enjoy!"

'Once again Brian O'Sullivan has created a thrilling historical drama. Liath Luachra provides strong ties to his other books (although each also stands alone very well). I think it's the depth of knowledge and research that adds the extra dimension that appeals to me but I really liked the fast pace, the developed relationships and the writing style.'

If you'd like to receive **Vóg, our somewhat lunatic monthly newsletter,** with articles on future projects we're working on, aspects of the creative process, bits and bobs on Irish mythology and more, please feel free to sign up at the Irish Imbas Books website

Printed in Great Britain
by Amazon